# EARLY LEARN TOGETHER
## SERIES
# TALK TOGETHER BOOKS
## The Bears in Oddland

ANNE MURRAY- ROBERTSON
ROBERT ROBINSON

ILLUSTRATED BY KATE SIMPSON

A Piccolo Original
Piccolo Books

First published in 1987 by Pan Books Ltd,
Cavaye Place, London SW10 9PG

9 8 7 6 5 4 3 2 1

© Anne Murray-Robertson, Robert Robinson 1987

Illustrations by Kate Simpson

ISBN 0 330 29853 4

Designed and typeset by
The Pen and Ink Book Co Ltd, London

Printed and Bound in Great Britain by
Springbourne Press Ltd, Basildon, Essex.

Produced by AMR for Pan Books Ltd

# A note to parents

This book is designed for you and your child to enjoy
together. The early learning activities form a natural
part of the story, so read it aloud to your child and then
talk about the pictures together. Don't push the child to
answer the questions, but give plenty of help and
encouragement.

By sharing the adventures of the bears in Oddland and
picking out all the odd things in the pictures, your child
is practising the very important skill of VISUAL
DISCRIMINATION. This means that he or she can
recognize different shapes, sizes, colours and so on,
which will help him or her with essential skills
necessary for early reading and early maths.

There are also a number of other useful activities which
you can do with your child in the home to reinforce
other early learning skills.

- sorting buttons for colour, shape or size
- matching shoes or socks for colours, patterns, size
- sorting the washing or ironing into piles for the
  family
- sorting the toys – soft, hard, new, old etc.
- sorting and matching crayons or pencils for colour
  and size

The Bear family were going out for the day.
Mr Bear was driving and next to him sat
Mrs Bear. Bumble and Grumble were in
the back of the car. They were very excited.
'When will we be there?' asked Bumble.
'Not long now,' replied Mr Bear.

The car began to climb up a very steep hill. Chug a chug chug, up a up up, went the car until it reached the top.

'We're there,' said Mr Bear, pointing to an enormous sign which said 'WELCOME TO ODDLAND.'

From the top of the hill, the Bears looked down onto Oddland.

Bumble and Grumble could see very odd things. Can you?

Mr Bear drove very carefully down the hill and round the bends. The car passed a sign and Bumble read it out. 'Take care! Animals crossing.'

'That's funny,' laughed Grumble. 'The cow on the sign has five legs. I wonder if we'll see one like that?'

At Oddland Farm there were some funny
things to see. Can you spot them?

'I think it's time to stop for a drink,'
said Mr Bear.
Mrs Bear agreed. 'A cup of tea would be
nice. Look out for a teashop,' she told
Bumble and Grumble.

'There,' shouted Grumble.
'Yes,' said Bumble. 'That must be a
teashop.'
'I wonder how you knew that,'
laughed Mr Bear.

Inside the Teapot teashop there were some
more odd things . Can you see them?

Back in the car there was a sharp bend ahead, and Mr Bear peeped the horn. 'Peep a peep, peep a peep,' went the horn and Grumble jumped with surprise.

'Oh Dad!' said Grumble. But she didn't have time to say more because they had arrived in Oddland village.

Oddland village really was odd and it
didn't take the bears long to find some very
odd things. Can you see them too?

When they arrived at Oddland Beach, Bumble and Grumble couldn't wait to paddle in the sea. Mrs Bear sat in her deckchair to watch. Mr Bear took a picture with his camera. 'Smile please!' he said.

This is a picture Mr Bear took with his
camera. Can you see some funny things in
the picture?

'We have one more place to visit before we go home,' Mrs Bear told Mr Bear.
'But I don't think Bumble and Grumble will want to go there,' said Mr Bear.

'Go where?' asked Bumble.
'To the fairground,' replied Mr Bear.
'Oh yes please, oh please, oh please, yes we do,' Grumble begged.

'What an odd fairground!' said Bumble.
Can you see some odd things in the
fairground?'

'What a busy day,' said Mrs Bear.
'I did enjoy it and we have seen a lot of
very odd things in Oddland.

Did you enjoy it Bumble and Grumble?'
But there was no answer. They were fast
asleep.